DELUXE EDITION
HOW TO HAVE **SEX** IN PUBLIC
WITHOUT BEING NOTICED

MARCEL FEIGEL
ILLUSTRATIONS BY BRIAN HEATON

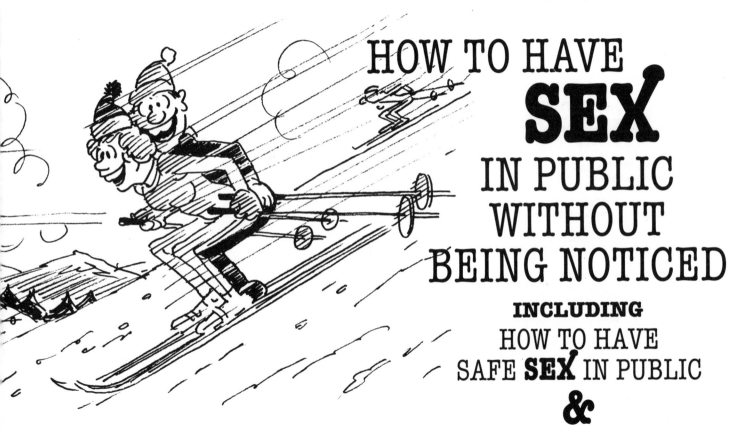

DELUXE EDITION

HOW TO HAVE **SEX** IN PUBLIC WITHOUT BEING NOTICED

INCLUDING
HOW TO HAVE SAFE **SEX** IN PUBLIC
&
HOW THEY USED TO HAVE **SEX**

The right of Marcel Feigel to be identified as Author of this work has been asserted by Marcel Feigel in accordance with the Copyright, Designs and Patents Act, 1988.

This edition first published in 1994 by Hutchinson.

135798642

How to Have Sex in Public Without Being Noticed first published in Great Britain in 1983 by Muller. Reprinted 1983, 1984 (twice), 1985 (twice), 1987 (twice), 1989 (twice), 1992 by Frederick Muller. Reprinted in 1993 and 1994 by Hutchinson.

How They Used to Have Sex in Public Without Being Noticed first published in Great Britain in 1987 by Frederick Muller.

Random House (UK) Ltd
20 Vauxhall Bridge Road, London, SW1V 2SA.

Random House Australia (Pty) Ltd
20 Alfred Street, Milsons Point, Sydney, NSW 2061, Australia.

Random House New Zealand Ltd
18 Poland Road, Glenfield, Auckland 10, New Zealand.

Random House South Africa (pty) Ltd
PO Box 337, Bergvlei, 2012, South Africa.

ISBN: 0 09 179166 9

Printed and bound in Great Britain by Clays Ltd, St Ives plc.

HOW TO HAVE SAFE **SEX**
IN PUBLIC WITHOUT BEING NOTICED

HOW TO HAVE **SEX** IN PUBLIC
WITHOUT BEING NOTICED

HOW THEY USED TO HAVE **SEX** IN PUBLIC WITHOUT BEING NOTICED

And when Noah looked out the Ark,

This is what he saw . . .

THANKSGIVING

BURIAL OF THE COUNT OF ORGAZ

WITH APOLOGIES TO EL GRECO

More tea, vicar?

Sometimes a man's gotta do...
what he's gotta do.

The Awakening Conscience

WITH
APOLOGIES
TO

WILLIAM
HOLMAN
HUNT

Meanwhile, back in the Foreign Legion . . .

England expects every man to do his duty.

It was twenty seven years ago